D1484190

Let Go

LET GO

a wordless novel

Mark Huebner

The Porcupine's Quill

Library and Archives Canada Cataloguing in Publication

Title: Let go : a wordless novel / Mark Huebner.

Names: Huebner, Mark, 19-8– author.

Description: 1st edition.

Identifiers: Canadiana (print) 2020031-242 | Canadiana (ebook) 20200317237 |
    ISBN 9780889844391 (softcover) | ISBN 9780889848771 (PDF)

Subjects: LCSH: Stories without words. | LCGFT: Wordless comics. |
    LCGFT: Wordless picture books. | LCGFT: Linocuts.

Classification: LCC PN6733.H84 L48 2020 | DDC 741.5/971—dc23

1   2   3   ·   23   22   21

Published by The Porcupine's Quill, 68 Main Street, PO Box 160,
Erin, Ontario N0B 1T0. http://porcupinesquill.ca

Edited by George A. Walker. Represented in Canada by Canadian Manda.
Trade orders are available from University of Toronto Press.

We acknowledge the support of the Ontario Arts Council and the Canada
Council for the Arts for our publishing program. The financial support of
the Government of Canada is also gratefully acknowledged.

For Caroline

FOREWORD

The high-pressure world of advertising is not for everybody.

You are expected to generate creative selling ideas every day. The money spent on those ideas can be jaw-dropping. Sometimes you are creating the biggest campaign of the year for a client, so a lot is riding on it. Sometimes you are creating a pitch campaign to land much-needed new business. And sometimes you are trying to save an account from walking out the door.

The pressure can be relentless.

Clients ride you hard because their jobs depend on how well you do yours. So you work twelve-hour days and weekends. Your love life gets the short end of the stick. Cold pizza at midnight is routine. You have the occasional smoke to calm the nerves. Your coffee cup occasionally holds something a little stronger than Maxwell House.

You have a thick skin because it is an industry built on rejection. For every idea that gets approved, a dozen more get turned down. To outsiders, the ad industry preens with too many award shows, but you know why they are critical. The awards are a calamine lotion for that constant rejection. But most of all, the industry needs to take its own temperature. The best work inspires you.

Along with awards there are rewards. It's an exciting, fast-paced business. You are paid well for sacrificing your nervous system. You can find yourself shooting a television commercial in Paris. Or Hollywood. You get to work with talented actors, eccentric directors, tasty photographers and testy celebrities. You drive a nice car. You enjoy legendary two-hour lunch hours. The people at your agency are comrades-in-arms. They work hard, they party hard. The shared foxhole creates strong bonds.

Every once in a while, you hit it out of the park. Your idea sells a ton of product and your client is thrilled. The agency president ducks by your office to give you an 'atta-boy'. The press writes about your work. People mention your ads at parties. Your campaign is judged best of the year by your peers and a shiny trophy is handed to you on a stage.

It's an interesting career because you travel light. Your tools consist of a pad and pencil. Doodling is high currency in this realm. You have an ability to observe human nature in a way few people do. You can be in a situation and hover above it at the same time. You are constantly analyzing your own behaviour. You take notes on why people do what they do, say what they say, think what they think.

You become a quick study. You are given reams of research to absorb with every new campaign. You do factory tours. You place bookmarks in product manuals. You learn to ask the right questions. You become adept at looking for a needle in a haystack of needles.

Your instincts are your stock-in-trade.

You love, honour, and obey your gut feelings. You climb the ad agency ladder because you are more often right than wrong. You know commercials can be annoying intrusions so you spend your career trying to make them fun. And smart. You pore over every syllable in a headline because you know the right word with just the right shade of meaning is the difference between being ignored and being persuasive. You become a consummate storyteller and can construct a tale within the unforgiving walls of thirty seconds. You are able to capture the essence of a product on a billboard in seven words or less.

You learn to put on your armour when you head into the boardroom. You know ideas are as fragile as soap bubbles. So you learn to fight for your work.

Your ads attract new business to your agency. The awards you win enhance the agency's reputation. You become a go-to person so you work even crazier hours. You daydream through conversations with your lover as you roll the latest assignment around in your head. You keep a notepad on your nightstand. You pull all-nighters.

You are all in.

Then one day, the economy slips sideways. Or a new director of marketing decides he wants a new ad agency for absolutely no valid reason. Or your salary is just north of a red line the new holding company has drawn. Or a new creative director is hired and wants to bring in her own troops. Or maybe you've sprouted a few grey hairs and that isn't a good look for a young, hip advertising agency.

That's when you are let go. You are shown the door with a cardboard box that contains the souvenirs of an advertising life: a favourite coffee cup, a cracked ashtray, and maybe a shiny award you won for the best commercial you ever did.

You don't retire from advertising. It retires you. That's when you have to let go. And move on.

Yes, the world of advertising is not for everyone.

Mark Huebner knows this crazy business better than anyone. Look for the delicious details in every single frame. And because he is a consummate storyteller, he doesn't need a single word to do it.

— Terry O'Reilly

Adman Terry O'Reilly is host of CBC Radio's *Under the Influence* and author of *This I Know: Marketing Lessons from 'Under the Influence'*.

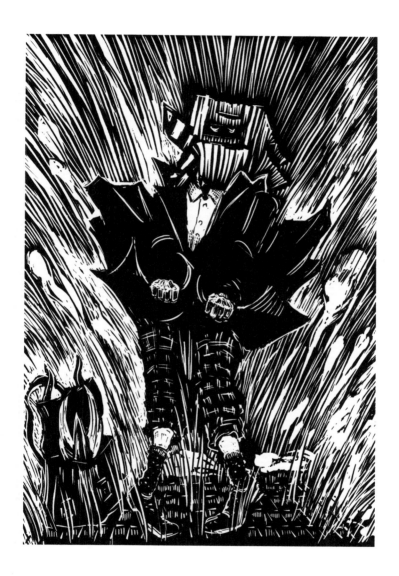

AFTERWORD

Reading pictures is not the same as reading text. We look at the preceding images and recognize some of the signs and symbols Mark has offered us. A snowflake, a lone man in a window, a box filled with office objects and an old typewriter. We know that the story must take place at another time in history because the typewriter is a relic from the 20th century. We try to comprehend the meaning of the images by forming a narrative around what we see. This is visual literacy. It's our ability to extrapolate a story from the signs, symbols and the language of representation offered by the images of people, places and things.

Mark has been a friend of mine for over fifteen years. We've worked together at a publishing house and socialized at the Arts & Letters Club in Toronto. We share an interest in the graphic novel and literature. I've been telling Mark for years about my fascination with the artists Frans Masereel (1889–1972), Lynd Ward (1905–1985) and Giacomo Patri (1898–1978) and their particular word-less storytelling process. Like me, they used printmaking processes known as wood engraving and linocut to create their wordless picture narratives. Linocut and wood engraving have similar graphic effect and Giacomo Patri was a master of the linocut. The process of linocut is literally cutting into flooring material with gouges and parting tools. I happily convinced Mark to explore this medium and create a wordless novel for our Porcupine's Quill series.

I introduced Mark to Patri's book *White Collar: A Novel in Linocuts*. The story follows a graphic artist and the injustices he faced in America after the market crash of 1929, all told in a sequence of 135 linocuts. Poignant and breathtaking in skill, there are similarities between Mark Huebner's narrative work and Patri's. The obvious one is the narrative of how a disruptive economic change impacts our ability to make a living. Huebner explores this narrative too but with new vision and a different approach to the impact of an unexpected economic and career change. He introduces the symbol of the office box full of stuff representing a lifetime of work and aspirations. A broken mug, ashtray, potted plant, radio, umbrella, broken cassette tape, and novelty letter opener are all stuffed into a box, not remarkable by themselves but together they are burdensome relics of a long-dead past. If we were to read into these symbols we might see the ash tray and broken mug as the accoutrements of an adman's wardrobe. They, along with a broken tape, represent long nights drinking coffee, smoking and listening to mix tapes trying to stimulate the creative juices to serve the corporate masters and present them with a campaign worthy of praise. But like the symbol of the Japanese enso, all we are left with at the end is a broken circle and a lifetime of events to reflect on—a box stuck on our protagonist's head leaving him blind to the future and anxious about a past he cannot change. But it is not all despair and lost hope—as you have seen—the box comes off, a friendly dog appears to save him and the story ends near a warm fireplace. If you look carefully, you'll see the broken mug and the picture of the girlfriend lying sideways on the floor. It's these little details that invite the reader to return to the linocuts to look for other symbolic clues and hidden narratives. That's where the joy of reading a visual narrative exists—in the details.

— George A. Walker

George A. Walker is an award-winning wood engraver, book artist and author who teaches courses in book arts and printmaking at OCAD University in Toronto, where he is an associate professor. He has eleven titles published with the Porcupine's Quill, the most current being a wordless biography of Mary Pickford.

ACKNOWLEDGEMENTS

Let Go was made possible thanks to my ex-employers and the support, help, and infinite patience of friends, family, and colleagues.

Thank-you, Caroline Felstiner, for listening to my ideas for a dozen grim endings to *Let Go* and suggesting that what this story really needed was a dog.

An overwhelming debt of gratitude is owed to George Walker for his vision, encouragement, and artistic support. He's always known me as a wordsmith and an illustrator who works with pen and ink and digital media. George ignored all that and believed that I could write a wordless novel as well as carve the images.

I have more gratitude than space allows to thank the exceptional people of The Porcupine's Quill. Many thanks to publisher Tim Inkster and editor Stephanie Small for their commitment to *Let Go* and their deft guidance. Throughout the journey of writing and engraving there was a chorus of support. This treasured ensemble included Anthony Harrison, Michelle Hogan-Walker, photographer Matthew Plexman and his partner, Sylvia Verkley, my daughter, Veronica, who bravely organizes my files, and, son, Mason who posed as the young writer and man lost in a blizzard.

Finally, I want to thank the astonishingly creative people I've had the joy of working with in advertising. The characters in *Let Go* are fragments of them and I hope the book does them justice.